Puzzle #1

MENACING

```
E  N  O  I  S  S  I  M  X  S  N  E  V  T  N
L  L  R  Y  X  Y  L  K  U  B  E  Z  R  F  E
L  U  I  I  S  E  X  A  Q  S  T  Q  U  H  U
C  F  C  S  I  I  I  O  I  F  C  R  K  D  T
W  O  X  U  S  E  O  O  D  C  L  U  B  S  R
S  E  N  A  T  I  O  N  A  L  I  G  L  G  A
C  Y  W  E  G  J  M  M  M  X  F  F  F  A  L
E  V  I  S  N  E  F  F  O  Y  E  V  F  J  R
U  K  X  D  J  Y  G  A  C  G  T  H  T  O  E
X  H  F  I  W  I  I  V  S  V  N  M  M  L  B
K  M  I  E  Y  S  Y  X  E  V  V  R  L  Q  D
V  N  Y  E  Y  C  K  P  P  T  J  C  L  B  V
F  O  N  D  X  Q  O  Y  D  U  A  G  E  T  H
U  R  N  G  K  V  E  V  Y  O  L  Z  O  C  I
T  O  T  C  Z  T  T  M  W  X  K  K  G  E  X
```

MISSILE	NET	OFFICIAL
MISSION	NEUTRAL	
MUSCULAR	NOISY	
NATIONAL	OFFENSIVE	

SHIVER

```
S  T  U  O  T  O  O  H  S  H  O  T  K  N  K
S  H  S  P  O  R  T  N  L  E  X  Z  A  J  M
T  K  O  X  V  P  F  K  U  Y  T  P  Y  L  P
Z  B  I  O  N  D  B  M  M  I  R  A  A  N  I
R  U  Q  R  T  N  S  A  P  U  J  U  K  S  C
G  P  L  M  M  S  L  A  S  H  I  N  G  S  V
F  S  P  I  H  I  S  T  A  N  L  E  Y  O  L
F  H  C  U  L  Y  S  S  T  G  T  H  C  P  V
E  R  U  A  I  X  N  H  Z  P  F  W  Y  C  T
X  H  P  X  F  A  Q  K  B  V  H  X  D  Z  S
P  A  U  M  R  I  G  L  F  G  W  C  H  W  Q
S  S  F  Z  C  D  I  V  P  K  I  E  R  D  C
Y  F  A  I  U  A  K  F  X  K  W  N  L  T  B
Z  C  R  L  G  Y  H  U  P  M  N  S  V  O  B
L  V  B  H  N  J  H  M  G  F  W  X  C  D  D
```

SHOOT	SKIRMISH	STANLEY
SHOOTOUT	SLASHING	
SHOT	SLUMP	
SKATES	SPORT	

EXPLODE

```
F  T  S  A  F  G  N  I  T  H  G  I  F  O  I
A  A  Y  S  F  L  A  I  L  O  F  F  G  N  Z
C  G  N  B  E  G  Y  F  O  R  C  E  F  U  L
E  D  D  S  F  N  D  I  L  E  R  I  F  V  I
H  Z  C  V  L  D  T  O  N  K  G  D  C  D  U
F  B  L  D  G  S  D  I  S  G  Z  S  G  Q  V
N  J  R  G  R  V  S  A  F  W  C  D  C  K  R
C  V  N  A  Y  Z  P  N  A  G  C  T  A  V  R
I  O  G  F  D  N  I  Y  J  L  P  G  V  O  M
I  W  Q  B  J  H  J  M  J  W  L  C  X  U  G
A  Z  O  L  E  T  A  I  J  O  X  N  J  G  F
M  R  V  A  F  O  J  G  O  L  A  U  P  W  A
M  V  C  A  K  V  F  H  I  F  S  O  X  B  S
K  S  S  M  R  V  B  X  I  X  A  U  N  Z  I
H  D  O  X  I  F  X  L  S  W  W  V  V  V  T
```

FACE	FITNESS	OFF
FANS	FLAIL	
FAST	FLYING	
FIGHTING	FORCEFUL	

OPENING

```
N T S E U N V E Z O O L I S G
G I S R C W I I M V V N N K A
V N G R O A S T Z A E W Y Q K
N C I I U O P H U T R K J W W
E S K D R B D W H I T G A E K
W S I E D O T T P O I E C X V
Z R E S S A P U U N M R B R T
T B Y C K I P Y O O E J H W R
S I S Y L A R A P Z U Q G R I
H P C A J A O G J A V M Q T M
N O X D U X N X R G A H S I H
Q B E L F N C J S H G M R V A
I H Q O E D L C E S X H A P C
Z X X T M P J S C X Q D K T N
O Z T R D I J O S K L B G Y C
```

ORIGIN   OVERTIME   PASSER
OUTBURST   PACE
OUTDOORS   PADDING
OVATION   PARALYSIS

TEAM

```
T  E  A  M  W  O  R  K  T  E  I  T  V  R  J
H  E  Y  U  F  Y  N  E  T  H  V  R  S  E  B
R  W  A  H  L  B  X  F  N  A  W  E  A  Z  H
E  V  Y  M  P  T  A  Q  J  I  T  A  D  H  D
A  W  U  L  M  O  I  P  D  U  A  S  R  B  S
T  B  L  E  A  A  R  M  R  J  U  R  S  T  P
E  J  W  C  A  P  T  T  A  U  J  E  T  I  S
N  Q  J  B  S  X  Q  E  C  T  U  T  Z  L  T
I  J  I  V  M  U  F  V  S  S  E  S  T  T  F
N  C  A  Q  X  P  P  E  N  M  E  X  L  Q  Y
G  J  V  C  H  Y  Y  G  J  H  F  Z  U  G  V
C  T  A  Q  N  V  U  E  Z  L  Y  O  I  S  C
O  Z  B  O  J  L  S  Z  T  G  N  Q  C  O  E
O  X  G  Z  G  P  T  L  V  H  S  B  W  G  U
M  I  I  N  H  L  O  H  H  C  S  B  Q  E  J
```

TEAMMATES	TEAMWORK	THREATENING
THWART	TIE	TRAINER
TROPHY	ULTIMATE	

FORWARD

```
F R A C T U R E Y N E Z O R F
F R E E Z I N G R Z E M A G E
T E L T N U A G Y A N H X U K
D E T F I G S K U R E E R Y I
Q L D O T M Y Y N V O G R Z S
T H J T G Z N K O E C L R F C
Z A T W A R N D M N L H G L F
T P D P G A N A C U R Y S Z Z
B F W V Q E D X S Y A X Y N G
M P I V S V U H W D K U A E Y
B T U G O N X M S Y A V I L L
I Z C M R P W P B T N B Q P D
F S W P N M E J N B I N O T W
V A D V R E X E X F H J H Q D
Y O J C J Z Z F T I X J C H Q
```

FRACTURE	GAME	GLORY
FREEZING	GAUNTLET	
FRENZY	GEAR	
FROZEN	GIFTED	

HOSTILITY

```
L  E  T  I  N  G  I  J  O  I  Y  X  V  N  N
I  O  M  F  M  H  H  R  J  M  T  Y  L  K  E
I  M  D  A  V  P  K  B  I  P  T  U  M  L  A
E  N  P  I  L  O  A  Z  U  R  U  F  G  C  R
L  C  D  U  S  F  L  C  W  O  I  K  J  R  F
P  S  N  U  L  J  N  H  T  V  P  R  W  C  W
E  C  S  E  S  S  U  I  W  I  Z  M  H  W  W
H  S  C  H  U  T  I  B  H  S  S  S  X  K  P
D  E  J  S  J  L  R  V  O  E  A  V  D  B  T
V  P  B  E  I  N  F  I  E  U  K  W  G  E  U
N  H  H  N  L  B  W  N  O  N  D  Z  O  C  Y
R  A  Q  L  I  Y  N  J  I  U  Q  Y  K  K  U
I  Z  G  H  R  K  K  W  F  J  S  K  Z  J  X
M  R  P  M  T  D  R  B  H  E  G  R  J  Q  W
E  W  Y  Y  N  M  T  R  U  L  M  A  X  S  H
```

IDOL	IGNITE	IMPACT
IMPROVISE	IMPULSIVE	INDUSTRIOUS
INFLAME	INFLUENCE	

PROVOCATION

```
K Y L Q U E S T Q T R R K H L
D C T L U R B Y U C E A F P W
F R U I E I L T A T Y K L N J
I U O P L U C U R I U C C L W
T J B C J A Q K R Z P A S A Y
K R V I E T U E I S G O N R
Z U I S O R P Q L R B U V G I
K O H Y C K V S L R J Z C B D
P F V W A W I F O R R Q D Q B
Y L S B U K Y X C H J N N B N
K W D J K K P E F O C I W R X
O S U M Q I Y U H Y H N B V R
F Y B G C D O M Z Y J G D K U
Z P C V X Z T D K D Y U Y M A
H C Z D O K H H B X P X Y G B
```

PUCK	QUEST	RECORD
QUALITY	QUICK	
QUARREL	RACKET	
QUELL	RALLY	

INJURIES

```
S  T  C  N  I  T  S  N  I  E  E  W  J  K  J
B  J  G  M  N  E  J  R  P  G  R  R  E  E  U
K  I  N  C  T  X  L  U  O  V  M  I  E  E  B
T  Z  T  J  E  T  F  T  B  I  S  S  R  N  I
Q  Y  U  A  R  D  S  L  S  I  N  X  I  A  L
M  W  W  E  N  F  D  E  R  O  L  U  U  N  A
M  X  M  Y  A  I  H  S  D  H  J  A  J  W  T
E  B  Z  V  T  V  Q  J  W  V  A  Q  N  L  I
T  Q  A  V  I  W  M  N  C  Q  I  I  F  T  O
Q  C  H  T  O  T  K  S  R  F  O  O  B  Q  N
T  H  A  F  N  U  D  X  V  G  X  U  C  P  M
S  D  X  C  A  B  S  C  Y  Y  B  F  Y  W  K
J  H  B  E  L  Q  C  A  R  C  Q  X  W  V  R
T  K  S  W  U  E  P  Q  F  P  P  M  B  E  B
O  P  K  I  R  L  L  T  H  G  D  L  M  K  U
```

INSTINCTS	JOSTLE	KEEN
INTERNATIONAL	JUBILANT	
IRE	JUBILATION	
JEER	JUNIORS	

HIGH

```
F A M E L L A H Y R T Q V Q C
S O A I M A D O O R O O P O S
J T C X O A E L L C O N O F I
J N I G B T D L E O K T O H Y
D H L C L K M E Z I V E S H Y
R W X H K H G R B P Y D Y I R
T X D L W I T E I B H X N T H
D E M C Z A N G B H N W J Y H
D T L K M N Y G O G Q Y E H J
U Z Q V E G X U S K E K Y N A
L E B S F W O T G C R U A W G
M G Q T B J C P Q L F A K C B
H W L E G A V W M R Q F U O S
X K T I M O Q J J H U T M V F
T U N T U W G F O Y N H S Y U
```

FAME	HALL	HISTORY
HOCKEY	HOLLER	HONOR
HOOT	STICKING	

UNIFORMS

```
E  L  B  A  T  C  I  D  E  R  P  N  U  V  V
Y  Y  S  V  O  L  A  T  I  L  E  C  L  I  I
E  C  T  U  V  O  W  Z  M  K  I  B  Z  C  O
C  L  N  I  O  Y  R  O  J  R  O  O  L  T  L
E  S  B  E  C  R  E  S  L  T  Z  L  Q  O  E
C  W  H  A  G  O  E  U  V  B  Z  P  Q  R  N
W  A  B  K  R  R  L  F  S  Q  A  Z  S  Y  C
M  I  E  W  L  E  U  E  I  A  C  Y  L  Z  E
C  V  G  Y  P  J  N  Z  V  C  E  H  K  C  X
H  J  F  M  J  A  Z  L  R  K  O  S  F  N  H
D  X  S  I  A  A  E  J  U  R  P  V  T  I  G
S  A  Y  W  C  X  O  W  O  V  H  M  G  P  B
Z  I  D  I  F  S  X  R  W  F  R  W  I  W  W
D  W  A  F  O  G  H  A  M  M  P  C  P  F  J
U  C  T  Q  C  D  W  A  Q  H  W  E  C  R  U
```

UNPREDICTABLE	VIOLENCE	VULNERABLE
URGENCY	VOCIFEROUS	
VELOCITY	VOLATILE	
VICTORY	VOW	

DISRUPTION

```
D  E  L  I  G  I  B  I  L  I  T  Y  E  E  E
O  E  L  N  N  F  Y  E  Q  H  B  N  Q  V  X
M  B  N  E  O  O  V  R  V  H  H  G  U  A  E
I  F  C  F  C  I  I  K  Q  U  E  E  I  L  R
N  J  L  L  O  T  T  T  K  O  Y  R  P  U  C
A  G  N  P  I  R  R  U  R  F  L  Z  M  A  I
T  J  T  U  U  F  C  I  C  E  T  W  E  T  S
E  H  H  F  W  J  P  E  F  E  X  L  N  E  E
J  Y  I  H  R  Q  M  V  P  Y  X  E  T  K  H
J  C  I  U  B  Q  B  L  Y  S  I  E  A  J  D
Y  V  S  J  X  Z  F  R  E  W  H  N  N  W  A
M  D  U  Z  P  O  W  Z  P  V  D  K  G  C  U
J  S  M  S  J  J  H  S  E  F  Z  G  B  D  Q
F  K  J  G  Y  J  X  B  F  W  R  L  J  D  E
A  N  C  H  W  L  Q  N  J  R  X  Y  W  C  P
```

DOMINATE	EQUIPMENT	EXERTION
ELECTRIFYING	EVALUATE	
ELIGIBILITY	EXECUTION	
ENFORCE	EXERCISE	

DANGER

```
S G E C H U A P H D F K T S U
E U N S V C A A D E G U T E X
Q T O I N R T B G F N Y I A X
K U U R T E L A N E H T C S D
T S H P E N F Z P N R A V Z N
I I L D S G U E G S A H L S O
C N N Z B I N A D E I P T H I
Z Z U O Z U D A D M S D E H H
U B F V G F Y V D A B O D F D
S G M Y V B H I L N P G A Y Y
S U O R T S A S I D M G S J N
E N I L P I C S I D W Q Y R N
K Q I P D Y U O Q Z Z O A D Z
X F N O K K O V M Z Q B V X R
J A W Z W Q I T M R U E Q W U
```

DANGEROUS
DEFENSEMAN
DISPATCH

DAUNTING
DISASTROUS
DISPUTE

DEFENSE
DISCIPLINE

CUP

```
R S C N S T A T U S T T V Y T
M A D S T R A T E G Y A T H T
K G T M A S U R G E R Y P Q T
N A T S T A L E N T W N Y E O
A C E N I D R N F Q G W Y N B
I T F R S E E T I M Z E T O J
C W Q T T R E L T Z F F U S M
E E S R I S U C G S V G F X T
B T T M C W S D M N V E Q S D
N A W M S G X Y M Z A M C K P
Z O G V T A Z X V W L T L G R
C E F I F V R A B R P U R F Q
W I U B I O V C H U T I T P L
A D Y V B E T M H D L L X E L
U O F E C C B I B B V U U J U
```

STAR	STREAK	TAPE
STATISTICS	SURGERY	
STATUS	TALENT	
STRATEGY	TANGLED	

SALVAGE

```
E  S  E  S  N  I  H  S  Z  L  S  S  X  P  C
K  G  R  R  C  O  P  A  D  S  C  E  A  L  N
B  C  A  A  O  O  S  B  O  N  R  C  T  W  R
X  J  A  V  C  C  R  A  J  E  E  U  J  V  J
X  L  V  B  A  S  S  I  E  L  A  R  V  G  Z
P  L  D  Y  T  S  A  C  N  S  M  I  C  B  J
X  P  R  H  Z  E  C  H  R  G  I  T  U  D  G
Q  H  U  Y  Z  H  S  D  U  X  N  Y  M  P  D
T  P  I  X  A  T  E  K  K  X  G  L  D  X  Z
G  K  P  Y  W  Y  N  R  A  I  V  X  W  M  W
O  J  P  J  T  K  V  L  V  D  C  B  E  Z  O
J  W  T  L  P  B  I  I  J  Q  T  U  Z  E  S
O  P  U  Z  W  C  B  O  D  C  V  C  Z  H  F
N  V  T  K  Q  Y  H  B  Q  Y  Q  Y  R  X  F
G  O  Z  N  M  P  T  H  U  X  L  I  R  F  K
```

PADS	SCORING	SETBACK
SAVAGE	SCREAMING	SHIN
SCARS	SEASON	
SCORE	SECURITY	

GOAL

```
G  O  A  L  T  E  N  D  E  R  H  T  H  S  W
S  U  O  V  E  I  R  G  H  D  E  A  A  Q  Y
T  Y  A  K  C  E  H  C  K  E  A  T  R  H  L
X  R  S  R  N  C  T  J  Q  P  L  R  H  D  I
I  Y  I  U  D  C  A  N  G  H  T  M  E  Q  Z
C  R  D  C  F  N  K  Z  W  O  H  L  E  P  D
H  H  O  M  K  N  Q  M  G  F  Y  X  I  T  F
X  K  U  R  T  Z  I  Q  B  K  T  H  B  P  A
L  L  Q  S  I  Q  I  H  K  B  L  R  U  A  T
O  T  E  E  I  P  U  B  G  O  Q  S  L  Z  Z
O  L  C  C  M  D  V  B  S  W  I  Z  U  R  X
P  D  D  V  Y  D  Z  Y  T  M  K  A  D  S  W
A  T  N  M  F  T  R  Z  O  C  Q  H  P  L  Y
B  H  H  H  B  D  V  E  O  Y  P  Z  W  H  B
O  Z  I  Z  X  M  T  N  A  U  D  X  Q  I  I
```

CHECK	HARD	TRICK
GOALTENDER	HAT	
GRIEVOUS	HEALTHY	
GUARD	HELMET	

POSITION

```
T R E P R E M E D I T A T E D
P S E C T N E I C I F O R P Z
R E O W I Y O P L A Y C C Z R
I A T P O T K I U Q K L G F G
Z S E L L P C Y T Z P B O T B
E O W A H E U A O C F Z R M F
U N X U Y X H Y R O E E N D S
Q G P J S N B O T P J T U A Z
O R O Z Y X M Z N R T N O J M
D O U G U R W O V A J R E R D
Z Z X F F J G L Y M B N N H P
Z U S U U C E R T U Y Q R D Y
M O X K J O O K C C B E K Z I
Y M N Z G D Z M X Y B O F Z S
R R A K G Z D E F J C C M Q A
```

PLAY   PREMEDITATED   SEASON
POST   PRIZE
POWER   PROFICIENT
PRACTICE   PROTECTION

LAMENT

```
L A U N C H E S G N I S O L M
L O S S M A I M R K E X Z Z A
D E U V U A N B O E S B Q Y Y
F B C L I W N J B S K A L X H
E T E I U A B A B Z H C M V E
Z I F Z D L J D G H X T O I M
N J G S L F S A S E A J A L R
Z W J C I U V Z O R R S G O K
T I P N D S S U I X L L U D L
R X G P V I N J E K W L P Y Z
Y I H I O U D C Y J B N H H Z
V V C K R Q J H C L A O O O E
C H H G K V U H U S I U P V J
J Q X Y Y O L T S U B Y D O E
J C Y C C H G S E D R N Q I O
```

LAUNCH	LOSS	MAYHEM
LOATHSOME	MAIM	
LOCKERS	MANAGER	
LOSING	MASK	

PASSION

```
P  A  S  T  I  M  E  D  Y  A  L  P  J  S  J
L  L  X  E  S  T  N  I  O  P  R  E  K  A  M
A  A  A  D  I  C  X  T  K  I  I  G  B  X  L
Y  Q  C  Y  X  T  D  E  Z  K  R  I  B  F  S
E  H  R  I  O  R  L  O  Z  C  A  E  S  Q  Q
R  X  W  D  S  F  J  A  E  W  L  N  P  D  V
S  Y  L  E  G  Y  F  B  N  U  Y  Y  Z  Z  Y
C  S  H  I  Y  H  H  S  D  E  W  Y  Q  A  G
R  Y  L  H  L  P  O  P  Y  W  P  X  W  A  U
O  L  S  F  C  G  I  M  C  E  P  W  K  C  W
V  T  L  N  J  G  F  J  C  I  P  P  L  T  Y
I  Y  F  Z  L  D  Z  R  A  R  V  I  A  V  J
F  I  P  T  O  J  N  Q  T  O  B  H  Z  W  K
L  F  Y  F  E  U  F  Y  B  O  B  S  D  S  S
B  W  Z  R  S  K  T  Y  A  E  G  O  R  E  P
```

MAKER   PHYSICAL   POINTS
PASTIME   PLAY
PENALTIES   PLAYERS
PERIOD   PLAYOFFS

SETTING

```
T  R  T  R  G  X  N  R  R  H  E  Q  J  F  A
R  N  E  F  I  Z  R  E  E  C  G  D  V  C  C
I  U  E  T  I  N  W  T  V  R  K  U  I  S  F
Y  Q  T  M  A  R  K  I  E  L  I  K  O  S  P
X  Y  Y  H  T  L  H  R  R  J  J  V  Y  R  D
F  K  G  U  L  I  I  E  E  G  Z  F  P  K  N
A  A  P  H  U  E  U  A  D  S  X  J  M  Y  A
L  K  R  W  N  A  S  R  T  F  M  O  K  X  Q
E  T  M  Q  B  J  V  S  C  I  R  W  S  H  W
A  Q  A  A  B  X  N  B  N  E  O  J  A  G  C
L  E  R  U  M  K  N  X  Z  E  R  N  R  M  U
A  H  J  V  C  D  C  A  I  Z  S  I  B  Y  D
P  D  T  I  B  T  P  C  L  B  R  S  R  M  I
I  D  H  K  I  P  C  P  K  D  Q  O  V  R  T
V  F  B  B  N  L  Y  P  I  E  I  I  R  N  R
```

RECRUITMENT	RIFT	SIDE
RETALIATION	RINK	
RETIRE	ROUGH	
REVERED	RUTHLESSNESS	

MENACING
Puzzle # 1

E	N	O	I	S	S	I	M			N			N
	L		Y			L	U	E		E			E
		I		S			A		S	T			U
			S		I			I		C			T
				S		O		C	U				R
	N	A	T	I	O	N	A	L	I		L		A
					M					F		A	L
E	V	I	S	N	E	F	F	O				F	R
									O				

SHIVER
Puzzle # 2

S	T	U	O	T	O	O	H	S	H	O	T		
S	H	S	P	O	R	T		L	E				
	K	O						U		T			
		I	O					M		A			
			R	T			P				K		
				M	S	L	A	S	H	I	N	G	S
					I	S	T	A	N	L	E	Y	
					S								
						H							

EXPLODE
Puzzle # 3

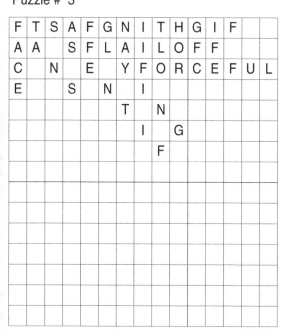

F	T	S	A	F	G	N	I	T	H	G	I	F
A	A		S	F	L	A	I	L	O	F	F	
C		N		E		Y	F	O	R	C	E	F	U	L
E			S		N		I					
					T		N					
					I		G					
					F							

OPENING
Puzzle # 4

N	T	S	E					O	O		
G	I	S	R	C				V	V		
	N	G	R	O	A			A	E		
		I	I	U	O	P		T	R		
			D	R	B	D		I	T		
			D	O	T	T		O	I		
	R	E	S	S	A	P	U	U	N	M	
					P		O	O	E		
S	I	S	Y	L	A	R	A	P			

TEAM
Puzzle # 5

T	E	A	M	W	O	R	K	T	E	I	T
H	E	Y	U				E		H		
R	A	H	L			N		W			
E		M	P	T			I		A		
A		M	O	I				A		R	
T			A	R	M			R		T	
E			T	T	A		T				
N				E		T					
I				S		E					
N											
G											

FORWARD
Puzzle # 6

F	R	A	C	T	U	R	E	Y	N	E	Z	O	R	F
F	R	E	E	Z	I	N	G	R	Z	E	M	A	G	
T	E	L	T	N	U	A	G	Y	A	N				
D	E	T	F	I	G				R	E	E			
								O	G	R				
									L		F			
								G						

HOSTILITY
Puzzle # 7

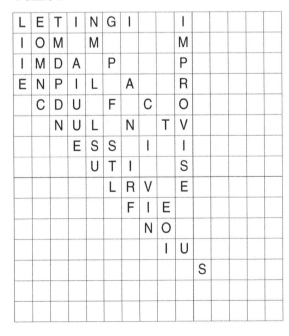

L	E	T	I	N	G	I			I
I	O	M		M				M	
I	M	D	A		P			P	
E	N	P	I	L		A		R	
	C	D	U		F		C		O
		N	U	L		N		T	V
		E	S	S		I		I	
		U	T	I		S			
		L	R	V		E			
		F	I	E					
		N	O						
		I	U						
			S						

PROVOCATION
Puzzle # 8

K	Y	L	Q	U	E	S	T	Q	T	R	
D	C	T	L	U			U	E	A		
R	U	I	E	I		A		K	L		
O	P	L	U	C	R		C	L			
C		A	Q	K	R			A	Y		
E	U	E		R					R		
R	Q	L									

INJURIES
Puzzle # 9

S	T	C	N	I	T	S	N	I	E			J	K	J
	N	E	J	R			R			E	E	U		
		T		L	U	O			I	E	E	B		
		E			T	B	I			R	N	I		
		R				S	I	N				L		
		N				O	L	U				A		
		A				J	A	J				T		
		T						N				I		
		I							T		O	N		
		O										N		
		N												
		A												
		L												

HIGH
Puzzle # 10

F	A	M	E	L	L	A	H	Y	R	T			
S							O	O	R	O	O		
	T				L		C	O	N	O			
		I			L		K	T	O	H			
			C		E			E	S	H			
				K	R			Y	I				
					I						H		
				N									
				G									

UNIFORMS
Puzzle # 11

E	L	B	A	T	C	I	D	E	R	P	N	U	V	V
Y	Y	S	V	O	L	A	T	I	L	E			I	I
E	C	T	U	V	O	W						C	O	
	L	N	I	O								T	L	
	B	E	C	R								O	E	
	A	G	O	E								R	N	
	R	R	L	F								Y	C	
		E	U	E	I								E	
		N			V	C								
			L			O								
			U				V							
				V										

DISRUPTION
Puzzle # 12

D	E	L	I	G	I	B	I	L	I	T	Y	E	E	E
O	E	L	N	N							Q	V	X	
M		N	E	O	O						U	A	E	
I			F	C	I	I					I	L	R	
N				O	T	T					P	U	C	
A				R	R	U	R				M	A	I	
T					C	I	C	E			E	T	S	
E					E	F	E	X			N	E	E	
						Y	X	E	T		T			
							I	E						
							N							
						G								

DANGER
Puzzle # 13

S	G	E		H				D			
E	U	N	S		C			E			
	T	O	I	N		T		F			
		U	R	T	E		A		E		
			P	E	N	F		P	N		
				S	G	U	E		S		
					I	N	A	D	E	I	
						D	A	D	M		D
							D	A			
								N			
S	U	O	R	T	S	A	S	I	D		
E	N	I	L	P	I	C	S	I	D		

CUP
Puzzle # 14

R			S	T	A	T	U	S	T			
	A		S	T	R	A	T	E	G	Y	A	
K		T		A	S	U	R	G	E	R	Y	P
	A		S	T	A	L	E	N	T			E
		E		I	D							
			R	S		E						
			T			L						
			I	S			G					
			C				N					
			S					A				
							T					

SALVAGE
Puzzle # 15

E	S	E	S	N	I	H	S			S	S		
K	G	R	R	C	O	P	A	D	S	C	E		
	C	A	A	O	O	S			R	C			
		A	V	C	C	R	A		E	U			
			B	A	S	S	I	E	A	R			
				T	S		N	S	M	I			
					E			G	I	T			
						S			N	Y			
							G						

GOAL
Puzzle # 16

G	O	A	L	T	E	N	D	E	R	H	T		
S	U	O	V	E	I	R	G	H		E	A	A	
T		A	K	C	E	H	C		E	A		R	H
	R		R						L				D
		I		D				T	M				
			C					H		E			
				K				Y				T	

POSITION
Puzzle # 17

```
T R E P R E M E D I T A T E D
P S E C T N E I C I F O R P
R E O W I   O P L A Y
I A   P O T   I
Z S       P C   T
E O       A   C
  N       R   E
          P   T
              O
              R
                P
```

LAMENT
Puzzle # 18

```
L A U N C H E S G N I S O L M
L O S S M A I M R K       A
    A     O E S       Y
      N     S K A     H
        A     H C M   E
          G     T O   M
          E     A L
            R     O
                    L
```

PASSION
Puzzle # 19

```
P A S T I M E D Y A L P
L L   E S T N I O P R E K A M
A A A   I       I
Y   C Y   T     R
E   I O   L     E
R     S F   A     P
S     Y F   N
      H S   E
        P   P
```

SETTING
Puzzle # 20

```
T R T R     R R H E
R N E F I   E E   G D
  U E T I N   T V   U I
    T M A R K I E   O S
    H T L   R R   R
    L I I E E
    E U A D
    S R T
    S C I
  N E O
E R N
    S
      S
```

SHIVER

OHOTS

_ _ _ _ _

UTSTOOHO

_ _ _ _ _ _ _ _

HSTO

_ _ _ _

ESTSAK

_ _ _ _ _ _

RKISSMHI

_ _ _ _ _ _ _ _

LHGNISAS

_ _ _ _ _ _ _ _

ULMPS

_ _ _ _ _

OSRTP

_ _ _ _ _

NYSTLEA

_ _ _ _ _ _ _

MENACING

IEISSML

_ _ _ _ _ _ _

IMONSSI

_ _ _ _ _ _ _

RULCAUSM

_ _ _ _ _ _ _ _

TAILAONN

_ _ _ _ _ _ _ _

TNE

_ _ _

RNTALUE

_ _ _ _ _ _ _

OISNY

_ _ _ _ _

IFFVSNEEO

_ _ _ _ _ _ _ _ _

ICFFOIAL

_ _ _ _ _ _ _ _

POSITION

STOP   _ _ _ _

NSSEOA   _ _ _ _ _ _

OREPW   _ _ _ _

APYL   _ _ _ _

ACCITERP   _ _ _ _ _ _ _ _

EDIRTPDEEAMT   _ _ _ _ _ _ _ _ _ _ _

IEZRP   _ _ _ _ _

FIOPNECIRT   _ _ _ _ _ _ _ _ _ _

TPTNIROOEC   _ _ _ _ _ _ _ _ _

OPENING

GNOIIR

_ _ _ _ _ _

RUSOUBTT

_ _ _ _ _ _ _ _

TDROOUSO

_ _ _ _ _ _ _ _

VIOONAT

_ _ _ _ _ _ _

IETERVMO

_ _ _ _ _ _ _ _

APCE

_ _ _ _

AGPIDND

_ _ _ _ _ _ _

RSAPLISYA

_ _ _ _ _ _ _ _ _

SARPES

_ _ _ _ _ _

PASSION

SMEATIP

_ _ _ _ _ _ _

NLTPEIESA

_ _ _ _ _ _ _ _ _

DREIOP

_ _ _ _ _ _

LPYAHICS

_ _ _ _ _ _ _ _

APLY

_ _ _ _

AMRKE

_ _ _ _ _

LEPRASY

_ _ _ _ _ _ _

YSOFFAPL

_ _ _ _ _ _ _ _

NTPSIO

_ _ _ _ _ _

PROVOCATION

KUPC

_ _ _ _

LUQTYAI

_ _ _ _ _ _ _

ARQULRE

_ _ _ _ _ _ _

EUQLL

_ _ _ _ _

SQETU

_ _ _ _ _

CUIQK

_ _ _ _ _

CTKEAR

_ _ _ _ _ _

YLLAR

_ _ _ _ _

CORRDE

_ _ _ _ _ _

UNIFORMS

EPIDAUNTERBLC   _ _ _ _ _ _ _ _ _ _ _ _

YEUGCRN   _ _ _ _ _ _ _

LEYTICOV   _ _ _ _ _ _ _ _

IOVCTYR   _ _ _ _ _ _ _

EILONVEC   _ _ _ _ _ _ _ _

UFVCSRIOOE   _ _ _ _ _ _ _ _ _ _

ITELLOVA   _ _ _ _ _ _ _ _

WVO   _ _ _

ARELBLVENU   _ _ _ _ _ _ _ _ _ _

DANGER

AESONGUDR

_ _ _ _ _ _ _ _ _

ATDUIGNN

_ _ _ _ _ _ _ _

NEEEFDS

_ _ _ _ _ _ _

NAEEDNSMEF

_ _ _ _ _ _ _ _ _ _

TOARSDIUSS

_ _ _ _ _ _ _ _ _ _

IELINISDCP

_ _ _ _ _ _ _ _ _ _

HPAIDTCS

_ _ _ _ _ _ _ _

IUDPSTE

_ _ _ _ _ _ _

TEAM

MMASETEAT

_ _ _ _ _ _ _ _ _

OAWKRMTE

_ _ _ _ _ _ _ _

EEGAINRHNTT

_ _ _ _ _ _ _ _ _ _ _

HTTRAW

_ _ _ _ _ _

IET

_ _ _

ATRRNIE

_ _ _ _ _ _ _

RHOTPY

_ _ _ _ _ _

TATUILME

_ _ _ _ _ _ _ _

OULNINCNVNAETO

_ _ _ _ _ _ _ _ _ _ _ _ _

GOAL

EORGLDANTE

_ _ _ _ _ _ _ _ _ _

SEOIUVRG

_ _ _ _ _ _ _ _

DRGAU

_ _ _ _ _

DHRA

_ _ _ _

HECCK

_ _ _ _ _

THA

_ _ _

KCRTI

_ _ _ _ _

TLYEAHH

_ _ _ _ _ _ _

LEHTME

_ _ _ _ _ _

HOSTILITY

DOLI   _ _ _ _

TIEGNI   _ _ _ _ _ _

CAIPTM   _ _ _ _ _ _

VSOIMRIPE   _ _ _ _ _ _ _ _ _

UEPVSIMIL   _ _ _ _ _ _ _ _ _

RCTRBLNEOTOVNIIE   _ _ _ _ _ _ _ _ _ _ _ _ _ _

SOUDINUSTRI   _ _ _ _ _ _ _ _ _ _ _

MIELFNA   _ _ _ _ _ _ _

NUEEFCINL   _ _ _ _ _ _ _ _ _

INJURIES

TINISTSCN   _ _ _ _ _ _ _ _ _

NEOLAITANINRT   _ _ _ _ _ _ _ _ _ _ _ _

EIR   _ _ _

ERJE   _ _ _ _

EOJTLS   _ _ _ _ _ _

TBILANUJ   _ _ _ _ _ _ _ _

IBJOUNLTAI   _ _ _ _ _ _ _ _ _ _

USOJRNI   _ _ _ _ _ _ _

ENEK   _ _ _ _

HIGH

KTCSIGNI

_ _ _ _ _ _ _ _

YRSTOHI

_ _ _ _ _ _ _

EOYCHK

_ _ _ _ _ _

ALHL

_ _ _ _

AMEF

_ _ _ _

OLLREH

_ _ _ _ _ _

ONORH

_ _ _ _ _

OHTO

_ _ _ _

CUP

RATS

_ _ _ _

ATSCTIITSS

_ _ _ _ _ _ _ _ _ _

USTSAT

_ _ _ _ _ _

TYAEGSTR

_ _ _ _ _ _ _ _

KSTREA

_ _ _ _ _ _

EGRYRSU

_ _ _ _ _ _ _

ALNETT

_ _ _ _ _ _

EATGNDL

_ _ _ _ _ _ _

APET

_ _ _ _

SETTING

NTEMTURIECR   _ _ _ _ _ _ _ _ _ _

TTRLANIIEOA   _ _ _ _ _ _ _ _ _ _ _

ERTEIR   _ _ _ _ _ _

DREEVER   _ _ _ _ _ _ _

IRTF   _ _ _ _

NIRK   _ _ _ _

IDSE   _ _ _ _

GUHRO   _ _ _ _ _

ELRTESNSHUSS   _ _ _ _ _ _ _ _ _ _ _

DISRUPTION

MIAONDTE

_ _ _ _ _ _ _ _

RELYFTENCGII

_ _ _ _ _ _ _ _ _ _ _

BIIYIIELLTG

_ _ _ _ _ _ _ _ _ _ _

NCFEOER

_ _ _ _ _ _ _

UMEQPEITN

_ _ _ _ _ _ _ _ _

AEVUALET

_ _ _ _ _ _ _ _

XNUECEIOT

_ _ _ _ _ _ _ _ _

CESERIEX

_ _ _ _ _ _ _ _

TEROENIX

_ _ _ _ _ _ _ _

SALVAGE

EGVASA

_ _ _ _ _ _

CASSR

_ _ _ _ _

CSOER

_ _ _ _ _

GCRIOSN

_ _ _ _ _ _ _

NMCSAREIG

_ _ _ _ _ _ _ _ _

NOSASE

_ _ _ _ _ _

RCSTIEYU

_ _ _ _ _ _ _ _

TECKASB

_ _ _ _ _ _ _

HINS

_ _ _ _

DSAP

_ _ _ _

EXPLODE

ACFE

_ _ _ _

FOF

_ _ _

ASNF

_ _ _ _

SFAT

_ _ _ _

TIGNHIGF

_ _ _ _ _ _ _ _

INTSEFS

_ _ _ _ _ _ _

IALLF

_ _ _ _ _ _

YFLIGN

_ _ _ _ _ _

CLRFFEUO

_ _ _ _ _ _ _ _

FORWARD

CAFTERUR

_ _ _ _ _ _ _ _

EFEZGINR

_ _ _ _ _ _ _ _

ZRNYEF

_ _ _ _ _ _

EZRFNO

_ _ _ _ _ _

MGEA

_ _ _ _

AULTGTEN

_ _ _ _ _ _ _ _

REGA

_ _ _ _

IDFGET

_ _ _ _ _ _

LRYGO

_ _ _ _ _

LAMENT

CANHUL

_ _ _ _ _ _

SHTLAOEMO

_ _ _ _ _ _ _ _ _

KLCROES

_ _ _ _ _ _ _

NOILGS

_ _ _ _ _ _

SLSO

_ _ _ _

AIMM

_ _ _ _

AGMANRE

_ _ _ _ _ _ _

ASKM

_ _ _ _

HMMAYE

_ _ _ _ _

SHIVER

OHOTS = SHOOT

UTSTOOHO = SHOOTOUT

HSTO = SHOT

ESTSAK = SKATES

RKISSMHI = SKIRMISH

LHGNISAS = SLASHING

ULMPS = SLUMP

OSRTP = SPORT

NYSTLEA = STANLEY

MENACING

IEISSML	=	MISSILE
IMONSSI	=	MISSION
RULCAUSM	=	MUSCULAR
TAILAONN	=	NATIONAL
TNE	=	NET
RNTALUE	=	NEUTRAL
OISNY	=	NOISY
IFFVSNEEO	=	OFFENSIVE
ICFFOIAL	=	OFFICIAL

POSITION

STOP	=	POST
NSSEOA	=	SEASON
OREPW	=	POWER
APYL	=	PLAY
ACCITERP	=	PRACTICE
EDIRTPDEEAMT	=	PREMEDITATED
IEZRP	=	PRIZE
FIOPNECIRT	=	PROFICIENT
TPTNIROOEC	=	PROTECTION

OPENING

GNOIIR	=	ORIGIN
RUSOUBTT	=	OUTBURST
TDROOUSO	=	OUTDOORS
VIOONAT	=	OVATION
IETERVMO	=	OVERTIME
APCE	=	PACE
AGPIDND	=	PADDING
RSAPLISYA	=	PARALYSIS
SARPES	=	PASSER

PASSION

SMEATIP = PASTIME

NLTPEIESA = PENALTIES

DREIOP = PERIOD

LPYAHICS = PHYSICAL

APLY = PLAY

AMRKE = MAKER

LEPRASY = PLAYERS

YSOFFAPL = PLAYOFFS

NTPSIO = POINTS

PROVOCATION

KUPC	=	PUCK
LUQTYAI	=	QUALITY
ARQULRE	=	QUARREL
EUQLL	=	QUELL
SQETU	=	QUEST
CUIQK	=	QUICK
CTKEAR	=	RACKET
YLLAR	=	RALLY
CORRDE	=	RECORD

UNIFORMS

EPIDAUNTERBLC   =   UNPREDICTABLE

YEUGCRN   =   URGENCY

LEYTICOV   =   VELOCITY

IOVCTYR   =   VICTORY

EILONVEC   =   VIOLENCE

UFVCSRIOOE   =   VOCIFEROUS

ITELLOVA   =   VOLATILE

WVO   =   VOW

ARELBLVENU   =   VULNERABLE

DANGER

AESONGUDR	=	DANGEROUS
ATDUIGNN	=	DAUNTING
NEEEFDS	=	DEFENSE
NAEEDNSMEF	=	DEFENSEMAN
TOARSDIUSS	=	DISASTROUS
IELINISDCP	=	DISCIPLINE
HPAIDTCS	=	DISPATCH
IUDPSTE	=	DISPUTE

TEAM

MMASETEAT	=	TEAMMATES
OAWKRMTE	=	TEAMWORK
EEGAINRHNTT	=	THREATENING
HTTRAW	=	THWART
IET	=	TIE
ATRRNIE	=	TRAINER
RHOTPY	=	TROPHY
TATUILME	=	ULTIMATE
OULNINCNVNAETO	=	UNCONVENTIONAL

GOAL

EORGLDANTE = GOALTENDER

SEOIUVRG = GRIEVOUS

DRGAU = GUARD

DHRA = HARD

HECCK = CHECK

THA = HAT

KCRTI = TRICK

TLYEAHH = HEALTHY

LEHTME = HELMET

HOSTILITY

DOLI	=	IDOL
TIEGNI	=	IGNITE
CAIPTM	=	IMPACT
VSOIMRIPE	=	IMPROVISE
UEPVSIMIL	=	IMPULSIVE
RCTRBLNEOTOVNIIE	=	INCONTROVERTIB
SOUDINUSTRI	=	INDUSTRIOUS
MIELFNA	=	INFLAME
NUEEFCINL	=	INFLUENCE

INJURIES

TINISTSCN	=	INSTINCTS
NEOLAITANINRT	=	INTERNATIONAL
EIR	=	IRE
ERJE	=	JEER
EOJTLS	=	JOSTLE
TBILANUJ	=	JUBILANT
IBJOUNLTAI	=	JUBILATION
USOJRNI	=	JUNIORS
ENEK	=	KEEN

HIGH

KTCSIGNI = STICKING

YRSTOHI = HISTORY

EOYCHK = HOCKEY

ALHL = HALL

AMEF = FAME

OLLREH = HOLLER

ONORH = HONOR

OHTO = HOOT

CUP

RATS = STAR

ATSCTIITSS = STATISTICS

USTSAT = STATUS

TYAEGSTR = STRATEGY

KSTREA = STREAK

EGRYRSU = SURGERY

ALNETT = TALENT

EATGNDL = TANGLED

APET = TAPE

SETTING

NTEMTURIECR	=	RECRUITMENT
TTRLANIIEOA	=	RETALIATION
ERTEIR	=	RETIRE
DREEVER	=	REVERED
IRTF	=	RIFT
NIRK	=	RINK
IDSE	=	SIDE
GUHRO	=	ROUGH
ELRTESNSHUSS	=	RUTHLESSNESS

DISRUPTION

MIAONDTE = DOMINATE

RELYFTENCGII = ELECTRIFYING

BIIYIIELLTG = ELIGIBILITY

NCFEOER = ENFORCE

UMEQPEITN = EQUIPMENT

AEVUALET = EVALUATE

XNUECEIOT = EXECUTION

CESERIEX = EXERCISE

TEROENIX = EXERTION

SALVAGE

EGVASA = SAVAGE

CASSR = SCARS

CSOER = SCORE

GCRIOSN = SCORING

NMCSAREIG = SCREAMING

NOSASE = SEASON

RCSTIEYU = SECURITY

TECKASB = SETBACK

HINS = SHIN

DSAP = PADS

EXPLODE

ACFE　　　　　=　　　　　FACE

FOF　　　　　=　　　　　OFF

ASNF　　　　　=　　　　　FANS

SFAT　　　　　=　　　　　FAST

TIGNHIGF　　　　　=　　　　　FIGHTING

INTSEFS　　　　　=　　　　　FITNESS

IALLF　　　　　=　　　　　FLAIL

YFLIGN　　　　　=　　　　　FLYING

CLRFFEUO　　　　　=　　　　　FORCEFUL

FORWARD

CAFTERUR	=	FRACTURE
EFEZGINR	=	FREEZING
ZRNYEF	=	FRENZY
EZRFNO	=	FROZEN
MGEA	=	GAME
AULTGTEN	=	GAUNTLET
REGA	=	GEAR
IDFGET	=	GIFTED
LRYGO	=	GLORY

LAMENT

CANHUL = LAUNCH

SHTLAOEMO = LOATHSOME

KLCROES = LOCKERS

NOILGS = LOSING

SLSO = LOSS

AIMM = MAIM

AGMANRE = MANAGER

ASKM = MASK

HMMAYE = MAYHEM

Made in United States
North Haven, CT
09 July 2023

38750248R00037